THE ILLUMINATING WORLD OF LIGHT

with MAX AXIOM
SUPER SCIENTIST

Emily Sohn

illustrated by Nick Derington

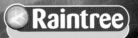

www.raintreepublishers.co.uk
Visit our website to find out
more information about
Raintree books.

To order:
☎ Phone +44 (0) 1865 888066
🖷 Fax +44 (0) 1865 314091
💻 Visit www.raintreepublishers.co.uk

Raintree is an imprint of Capstone Global Library Limited, a company incorporated in England and
Wales having its registered office at 7 Pilgrim Street, London EC4V 6LB
Registered company number: 6695882

"Raintree" is a registered trademark of Pearson Education Limited, under licence to Capstone Global
Library Limited

Text © Capstone Press 2008
First published by Capstone Press in 2008
First published in hardback in the United Kingdom by Capstone Global Library in 2010
The moral rights of the proprietor have been asserted.

ISBN 978 1 4062 1458 1(hardback)
14 13 12 11 10

British Library Cataloguing in Publication Data
Sohn, Emily
Light. -- (Graphic science)
535-dc22
A full catalogue record for this book is available from the British Library.

Art Director and Designer: Bob Lentz
Cover Artist: Tod Smith
UK Editor: Diyan Leake
UK Production: Alison Parsons
Originated by Capstone Global Library
Printed and bound in China by South China Printing Company Limited

Acknowledgements
The publisher would like to thank the following for permission to reproduce copyright material:
iStockphoto p. 23; Shutterstock p. 13 (Jo-Hanna Wienert)

Contents

With a sudden flash of lightning, Super Scientist Max Axiom begins an adventure in light.

CRACKK!..

What was that?

It's okay, Spark. It's just a little thunder and lightning from a passing storm.

WHIMPER...WHIMPERRR...

Actually, Spark, if you could understand how light works, things like lightning wouldn't be so scary.

4

Light is a type of energy. In fact, sunlight is our main source of energy on earth.

Don't believe me? Take a look at a typical food chain.

Plants use sunlight to make food in a process called photosynthesis.

This food allows plants to grow. Plants then provide food for animals.

In turn, these plant-eating animals are a food source for meat-eating animals.

As you can see, all life on earth depends on the sun's light, including us.

Let's check out how the sun makes this energy.

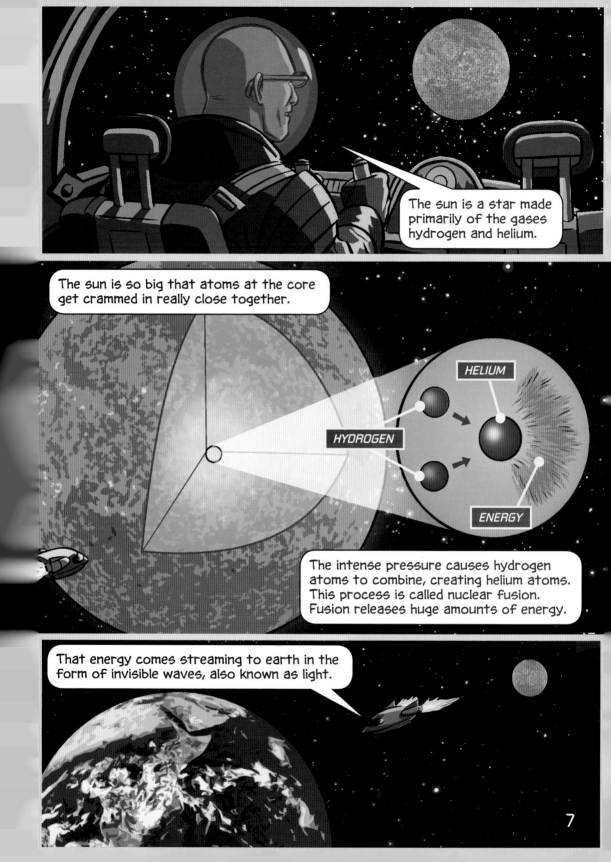

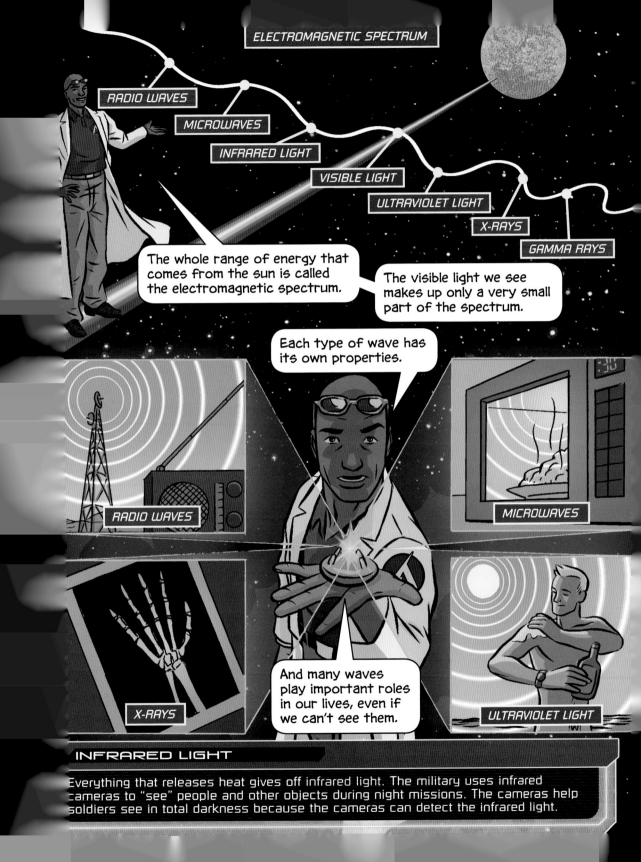

When white light passes through a prism it bends and splits apart. The prism shows us the colours of the rainbow that make up white light.

On the electromagnetic spectrum, red, orange, yellow, green, blue, indigo, and violet line up by the length of their waves.

Red has the longest wavelength you can see. Violet has the shortest wavelength.

Light has some other cool properties too.

ROYGBIV

Want to know more? Let's go for a ride!

Because opaque objects block light, we see shadows, or dark spots, behind them.

Of course, not all objects are completely transparent or totally opaque.

Some objects are translucent. For example, this stained glass window lets some light through, but we can't see through it to the other side.

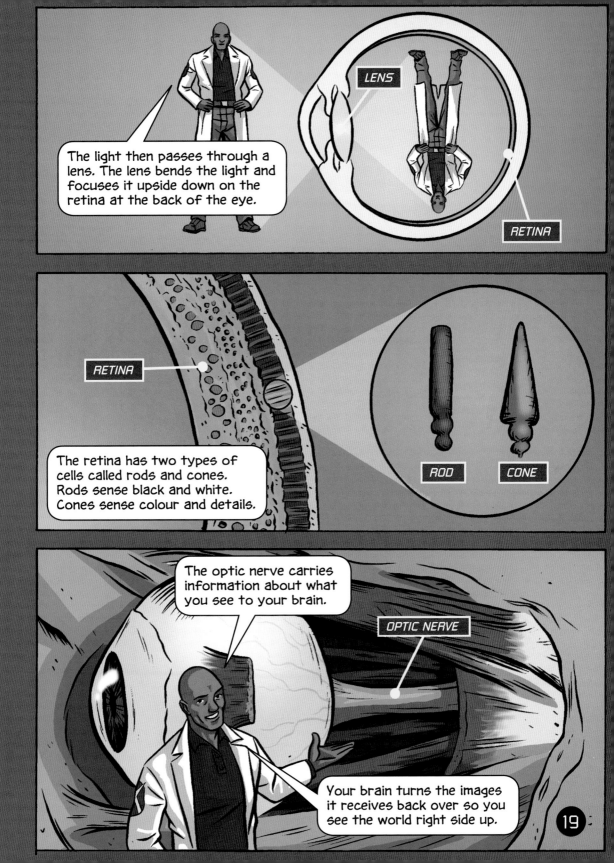

Short-sighted people see close objects clearly, but objects in the distance look blurry. They wear glasses with concave lenses to see clearly.

Far-sighted people see distant objects clearly, but objects that are close look blurry. They wear glasses with convex lenses to correct their vision.

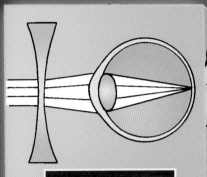

CONCAVE LENS FOR SHORT-SIGHTED EYE

CONVEX LENS FOR FAR-SIGHTED EYE

Magnifying glasses and microscopes use lenses too.

PLANT CELL

A magnifying glass uses a convex lens to make small objects look bigger.

A microscope uses two convex lenses to make things as tiny as plant cells appear bigger.

Laser light can be focused onto a very small spot, making it easy to aim. Some lasers are so powerful that they can cut through steel!

SSIZZLE

But less powerful lasers are used to play CDs and DVDs . . .

. . . do eye surgery . . .

BEEP!

. . . and scan bar codes.

MORE ABOUT LASERS

Lasers use mirrors to bounce light back and forth until it is all moving in one focused direction. The types of atoms inside a laser determine what wavelength will come out. Ruby-filled lasers give off red light. Carbon dioxide-filled lasers give off infrared light, which can be hot enough to cut metal.

Sunlight does a lot more than just let us see.

Sunlight, or solar energy, can become heat—enough heat to bake cookies in a solar oven.

Thanks for the cookies.

See you later, Max!

SOLAR CELLS

Solar energy can also be changed into electricity.

In fact, some homes collect power with solar cells.

25

MORE ABOUT LIGHT

Light from the sun makes the trip to earth in about 8 minutes and 18 seconds. Travelling the same distance in your car at motorway speeds would take more than 170 years.

Light changes speeds when it passes from one material to another. When light passes from air to water, it slows down to about 225,000 kilometres (139,800 miles) per second.

The colour of your T-shirt on a sunny, summer day can make a big difference in how hot you feel. Darker colours absorb more light than lighter colours. To stay cooler, wear a white T-shirt on a sunny day because it reflects more light than a darker shirt.

Only 10 percent of the energy used by a regular incandescent lightbulb is changed into visible light. The rest of the energy is wasted as heat.

Telescopes use lenses or mirrors to capture the little bits of light that come to earth from stars, planets, and galaxies in space. The Hubble Space Telescope has allowed us to see galaxies more than 12 billion light years away.

Human eyes can sense light only within the visible wavelengths on the electromagnetic spectrum. Some animals see the world in a completely different way. Rattlesnakes have sensory pits that detect infrared light. Bees see ultraviolet light.

 Moonbows are rainbows that form at night. These faint rainbows form when raindrops refract light reflecting off the moon. When moonlight refracts off ice crystals in the atmosphere, bright halos called moon dogs form around the moon.

 Solar energy powers satellites and spacecraft orbiting earth. The International Space Station's huge solar panels turn sunlight into electricity, light, and heat for the astronauts living and working on the spacecraft.

MORE ABOUT

SUPER SCIENTIST

Real name: Maxwell Axiom
Height: 1.86 m (6 ft 1 in.)
Weight: 87 kg (13 st. 10 lb.)
Eyes: Brown   Hair: None

Super capabilities: Super intelligence; able to shrink to the size of an atom; sunglasses give X-ray vision; lab coat allows for travel through time and space.

Origin: Since birth, Max Axiom seemed destined for greatness. His mother, a marine biologist, taught her son about the mysteries of the sea. His father, a nuclear physicist and volunteer park warden, showed Max the wonders of the earth and sky.

One day, while Max was hiking in the hills, a megacharged lightning bolt struck him with blinding fury. When he awoke, he discovered a new-found energy and set out to learn as much about science as possible. He travelled the globe studying every aspect of the subject. Then he was ready to share his knowledge and new identity with the world. He had become Max Axiom, Super Scientist.

Glossary

atom smallest form of any element

concave hollow and curved, like the inside of a bowl

convex curved outward, like the outside of a ball

energy ability to do work, such as moving things or giving heat or light

fusion joining together of objects caused by heating. The sun creates its energy with the process of fusion.

infrared light light that produces heat. Humans cannot see infrared light.

laser thin, intense, high-energy beam of light

opaque blocks light

reflection change in direction of light bouncing off a surface

refract bend light at an angle as it passes through a substance

translucent lets light pass through, but is not transparent. Frosted and stained glass are translucent.

transparent lets light through

ultraviolet light an invisible form of light that can cause sunburns

wavelength distance between two peaks of a wave

FIND OUT MORE

Books

Electricity: Turn It On!, Wendy Sadler (Raintree, 2005)

Experiments with Light, Rachel Lynette (Heinemann Library, 2008)

Fossil Fuels and Biofuels, Elizabeth Raum (Heinemann Library, 2008)

Light (Tabletop Scientist series), Steve Parker (Heinemann Library, 2005)

The Story Behind Electricity, Sean Price (Heinemann Library, 2009)

Voyage of a Light Beam, Andrew Solway (Raintree, 2005)

Website

www.bbc.co.uk/schools/ks2bitesize
Click on "Science" and then "Physical processes" for activities and quizzes on topics such as "Light and dark" and "Light and shadows"

http://news.bbc/co.uk/cbbcnews
Enter "light" in the Search field to find out how this topic has been in the news.

INDEX